Saxmania!
Classics.

Wise Publications
London/New York/Paris/Sydney/Copenhagen/Madrid

Exclusive Distributors:
Music Sales Limited
8/9 Frith Street, London W1V 5TZ, England.
Music Sales Pty Limited
120 Rothschild Avenue, Rosebery, NSW 2018, Australia.
Music Sales Corporation
257 Park Avenue South, New York, NY10010, U.S.A.

Order No. AM92021
ISBN 0-7119-4128-9
This book © Copyright 1995 by Wise Publications

Compiled by Peter Evans
Music arranged by Steve Tayton
Music processed by Ternary Graphics

Book design by Studio Twenty, London
Cover photograph by Julian Hawkins

Printed in the United Kingdom by
Halstan & Co Limited, Amersham, Buckinghamshire.

Your Guarantee of Quality

As publishers, we strive to produce every book to the highest commercial standards.
The music has been freshly engraved and the book has been carefully designed to minimise awkward page turns and to
make playing from it a real pleasure. Particular care has been given to specifying acid-free,
neutral-sized paper which has not been chlorine bleached but produced with special regard for the environment.
Throughout, the printing and binding have been planned to ensure a sturdy, attractive publication which should give years of enjoyment.
If your copy fails to meet our high standards, please inform us and we will gladly replace it.

Music Sales' complete catalogue lists thousands of titles and is free from your local music shop, or direct from Music Sales Limited.
Please send a cheque/postal order for £1.50 for postage to: Music Sales Limited, Newmarket Road, Bury St. Edmunds, Suffolk IP33 3YB.

And just look at some of the other music you can play with Saxmania!...

Saxmania! Standards
Includes 'Catch A Falling Star'...
'As Time Goes By'...'Pennies From Heaven'...
and 31 more golden favourites.
Order No. AM78262

Saxmania! Blues Greats
Includes 'Basin Street Blues'...
'Georgia On My Mind'...'Lazy Bones'...
and over 30 other essential blues numbers.
Order No. AM90099

Saxmania! Jazz Hits
Includes 'Mood Indigo'...
'Take The 'A' Train'...'Take Five'...
and two dozen more all-time greats.
Order No. AM78254

Saxmania! The Beatles
Includes 'Eleanor Rigby'...
'Hey Jude'...'Yesterday'...
and 32 other famous Beatles hits.
Order No. NO90462

Saxmania! Jazz Hits 2
Includes 'Anthropology'...
'Flying Home'...'Ruby, My Dear'...
and 28 more great jazz hits.
Order No. AM92022

Saxmania! The Beatles 2
Includes 'All My Loving'...
'Help'...'I Want To Hold Your Hand'...
and 34 more famous Beatles songs.
Order No. NO90573

Saxmania! Pop Greats
Includes 'Sailing'...'Stand By Me'...
'Nothing's Gonna Change My Love For You'...
and 29 more chart hits.
Order No. AM78247

Saxmania! Big Band
Includes 'A Taste Of Honey'...
'Night Train'...'Opus One'...
and 33 other Big Band numbers.
Order No. AM90122

Saxmania! Pop Greats 2
Includes 'Hope Of Deliverance'...
'Keep The Faith'...'Tears In Heaven'...
and 27 other hit songs.
Order No. AM91547

Saxmania! Great Solos
Includes 'Baker Street'...'Careless Whisper'...
'Lily Was Here'...'Your Latest Trick'...
and nine more stunning solos.
Order No. AM90123

Saxmania! Jazz Classics
Includes 'On The Sunny Side Of The Street'...
'Walking Shoes'...'Cute'...
and 30 other jazz classics.
Order No. AM90100

Saxmania! Ballads
Includes 'A Whiter Shade of Pale'...
'For The Good Times'...'Nights In White Satin'...
and 28 more all-time favourites.
Order No. AM91548

Saxmania! Rock Hits
Includes 'Addicted To Love'...
'Layla'...'Roxanne'...
and 20 other rock classics.
Order No. AM90101

Saxmania! Christmas Songs
Includes 'I Wish It Could Be Christmas Every Day'...
'Mary's Boy Child'...'Silent Night'...
and 36 more festive songs.
Order No. AM92007

Adagio Theme from Clarinet Concerto In A Major K.622 Wolfgang Amadeus Mozart *4*
Air from Water Music George Frideric Handel *6*
Aria from Orfeo Christoph Willibald Gluck *8*
Autumn from The Four Seasons Antonio Vivaldi *5*
Ave Maria Franz Schubert *10*
Ave Verum Corpus Wolfgang Amadeus Mozart *12*
Bourrée from Music For The Royal Fireworks George Frideric Handel *14*
Bridal March from Lohengrin Richard Wagner *16*
1st Movement Theme from Eine Kleine Nachtmusik K.525 Wolfgang Amadeus Mozart *18*
Emperor Waltz Johann Strauss II *11*
Für Elise Ludwig van Beethoven *20*
Hornpipe from Water Music George Frideric Handel *22*
Jesu, Joy Of Man's Desiring Johann Sebastian Bach *24*
Là Ci Darem La Mano from Don Giovanni Wolfgang Amadeus Mozart *26*
March from Scipione George Frideric Handel *28*
March from The Nutcracker Peter Ilyich Tchaikovsky *25*
Minuet Luigi Boccherini *30*
Minuet And Trio from Eine Kleine Nachtmusik K.525 Wolfgang Amadeus Mozart *32*
Minuet from Anna Magdalena Bach's Notebook Johann Sebastian Bach *31*
Morning from Peer Gynt Suite Edvard Grieg *34*
O, For The Wings Of A Dove Felix Mendelssohn *37*
Ode To Joy from Symphony No.9 Ludwig van Beethoven *36*
Theme from Romeo And Juliet Peter Ilyich Tchaikovsky *38*
See The Conquering Hero Comes from Judas Maccabaeus George Frideric Handel *40*
1st Movement Theme from Sonata In A K.300 Wolfgang Amadeus Mozart *41*
2nd Movement Theme from Symphony No. 9 (From The New World) Antonin Dvořák *43*
2nd Movement Theme from Symphony No. 94 in G (Surprise) Joseph Haydn *42*
Theme from Symphony In G Minor K.550 Wolfgang Amadeus Mozart *44*
Theme from Variations On A Theme By Haydn (St Anthony Chorale) Johannes Brahms *48*
Waltz from Die Fledermaus Johann Strauss II *46*

Adagio Theme
from Clarinet Concerto In A Major K.622

Wolfgang Amadeus Mozart (1756–1791)

Autumn
from The Four Seasons

Antonio Vivaldi (1675–1741)

Air
from Water Music

George Frideric Handel (1685–1759)

Fairly slow

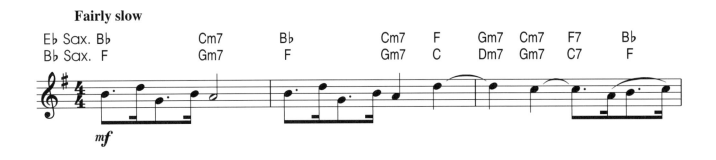

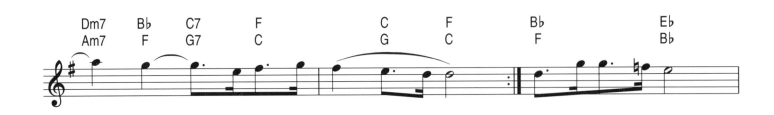

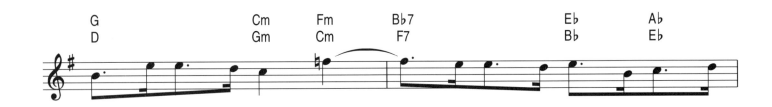

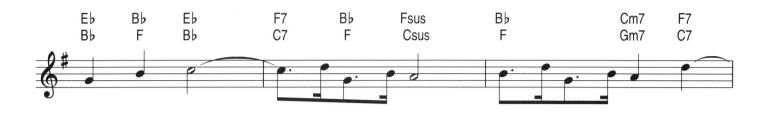

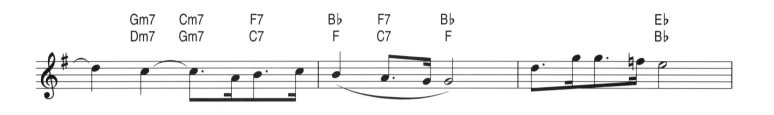

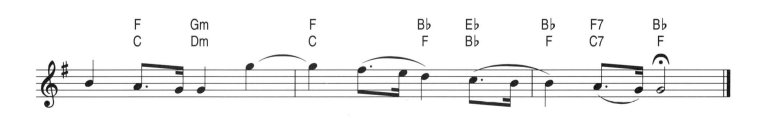

Aria
from Orfeo

Christoph Willibald Gluck (1714–1787)

9

Ave Maria

Franz Schubert (1797–1828)

Emperor Waltz

Johann Strauss II (1825–1899)

Ave Verum Corpus

Wolfgang Amadeus Mozart (1756–1791)

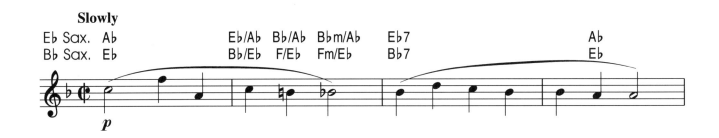

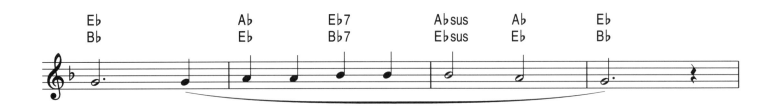

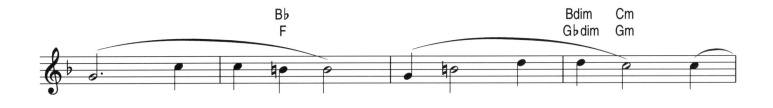

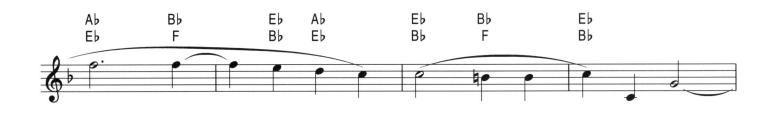

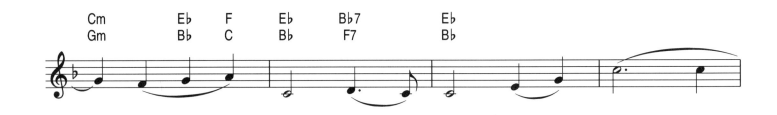

Bourrée
from Music For The Royal Fireworks

George Frideric Handel (1685–1759)

Allegro

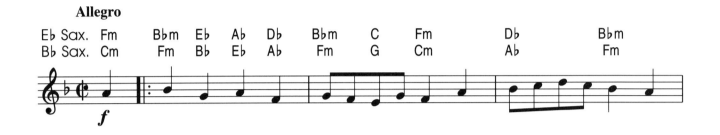

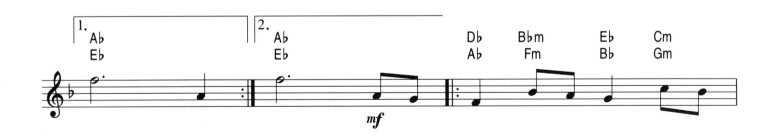

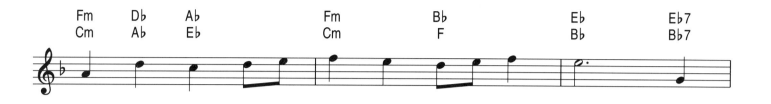

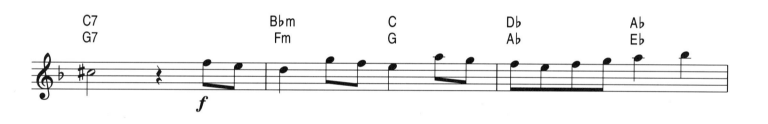

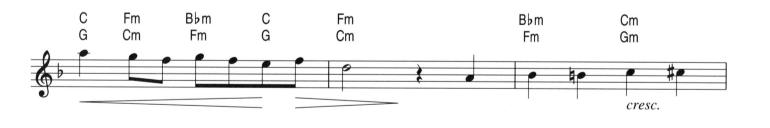

15

Bridal March
from Lohengrin

Richard Wagner (1813–1883)

CODA

1st Movement Theme
from Eine Kleine Nachtmusik K.525

Wolfgang Amadeus Mozart (1756–1791)

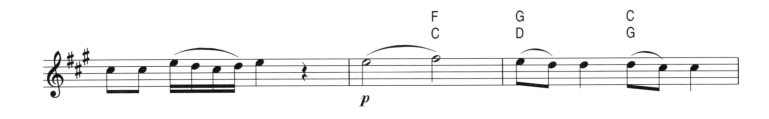

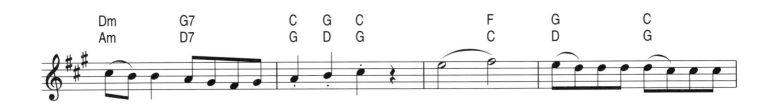

Für Elise

Ludwig van Beethoven (1770–1827)

Not too fast

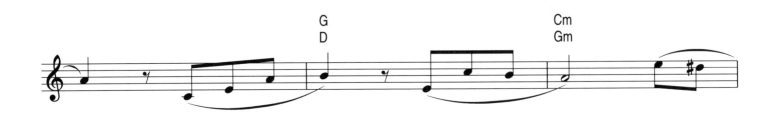

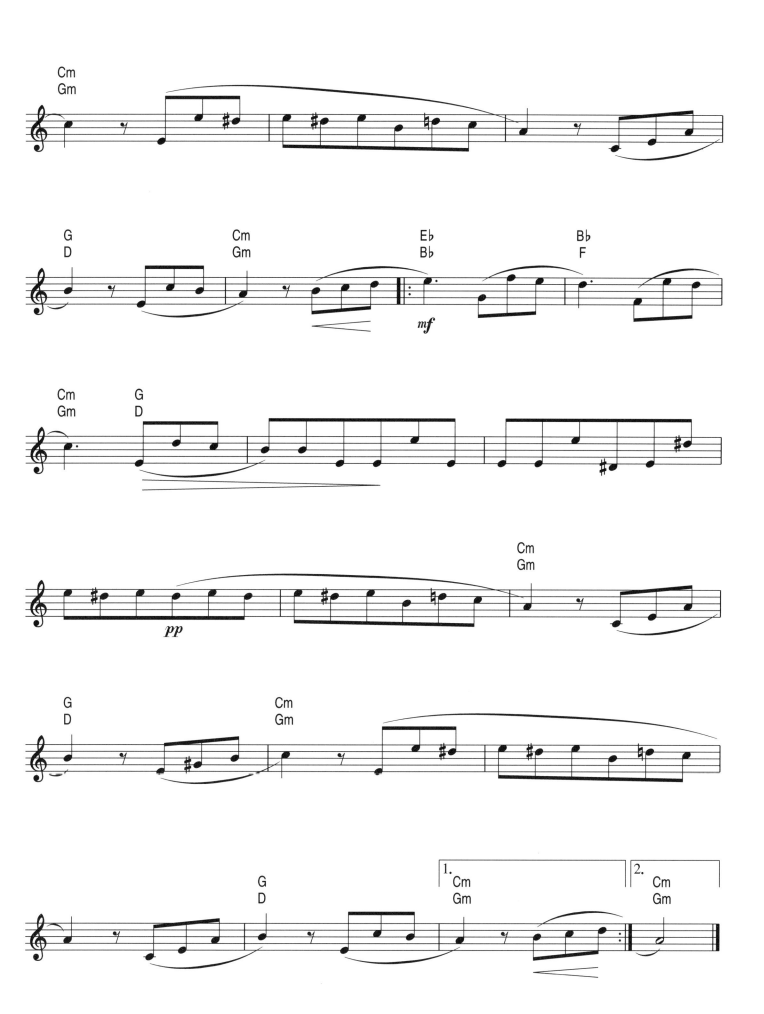

Hornpipe
from Water Music

George Frideric Handel (1685–1759)

Jesu, Joy Of Man's Desiring

Johann Sebastian Bach (1685–1750)

March
from The Nutcracker

Peter Ilyich Tchaikovsky (1840–1893)

Là Ci Darem La Mano

from Don Giovanni

Wolfgang Amadeus Mozart (1756–1791)

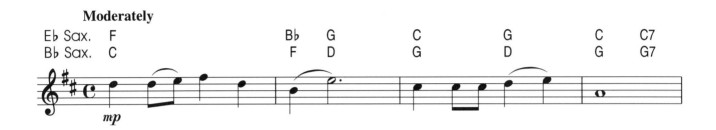

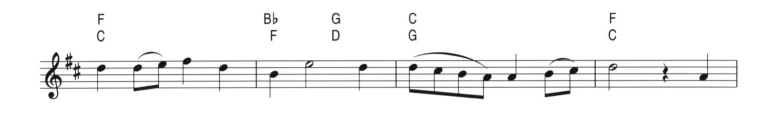

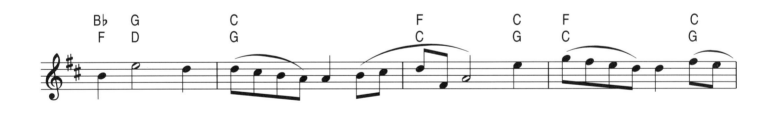

March
from Scipione

George Frideric Handel (1685–1759)

Minuet

Luigi Boccherini (1743–1805)

Minuet
from Anna Magdalena Bach's Notebook

Johann Sebastian Bach (1685–1750)

Tempo di minuetto

Minuet & Trio
from Eine Kleine Nachtmusik K.525

Wolfgang Amadeus Mozart (1756–1791)

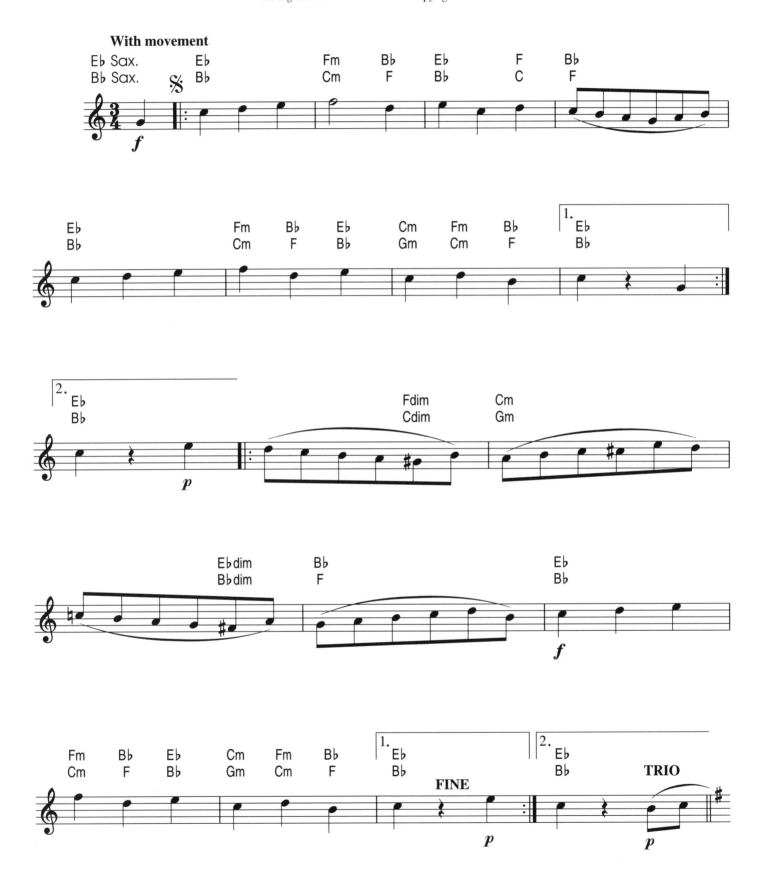

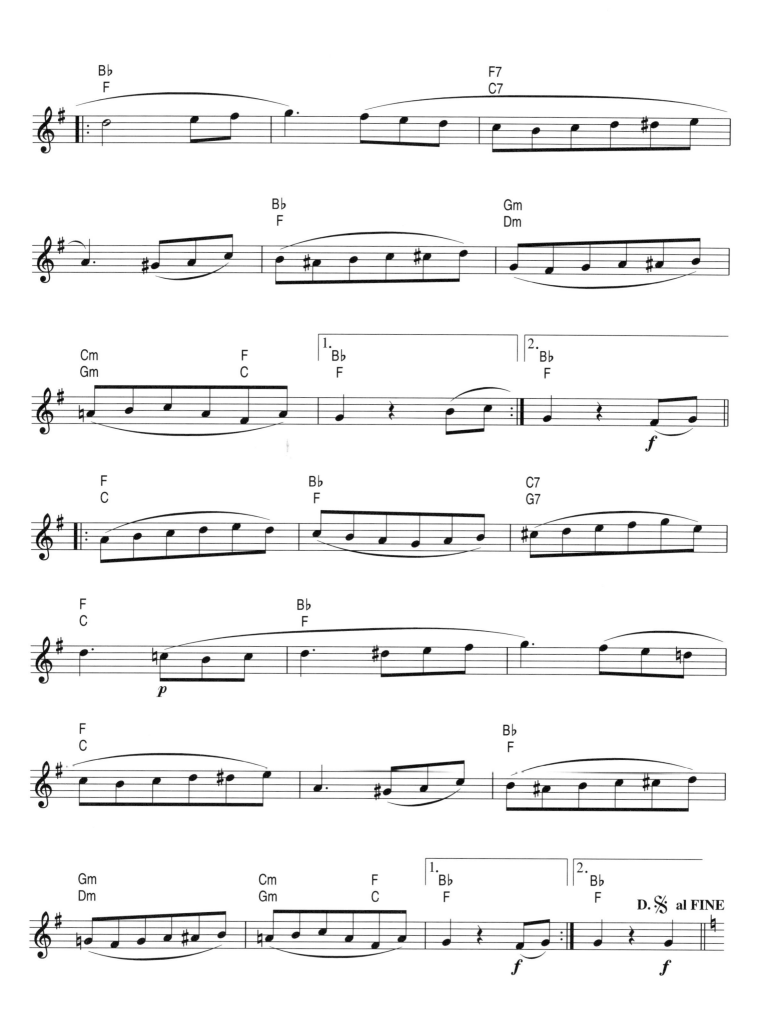

Morning
from Peer Gynt Suite

Edvard Grieg (1843–1907)

Ode To Joy
from Symphony No.9

Ludwig van Beethoven (1770–1827)

O, For The Wings Of A Dove

Felix Mendelssohn (1809–1847)

Theme from Romeo & Juliet

Peter Ilyich Tchaikovsky (1840–1893)

See The Conquering Hero Comes
from Judas Maccabaeus

George Frideric Handel (1685–1759)

1st Movement Theme
from Sonata In A K.300

Wolfgang Amadeus Mozart (1756–1791)

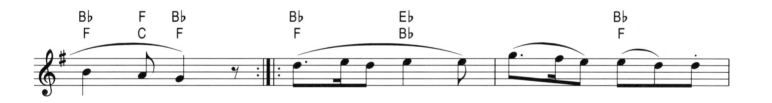

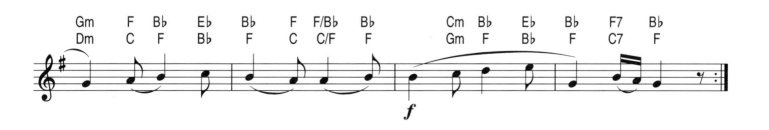

2nd Movement Theme

from Symphony No.94 In G (Surprise)

Joseph Haydn (1732–1809)

2nd Movement Theme
from Symphony No.9 (From The New World)

Antonin Dvořák (1841–1904)

Theme from Symphony In G Minor K.550

Wolfgang Amadeus Mozart (1756–1791)

With movement

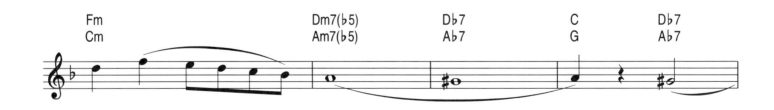

Waltz
from Die Fledermaus

Johann Strauss II (1825–1899)

Moderately

Theme from Variations On A Theme By Haydn
(St. Anthony Chorale)

Johannes Brahms (1833–1897)